When a MONSTER Dreams

By Cat Gayle
Illustrated by Joan Coleman

BOOKLOGIX KIDS

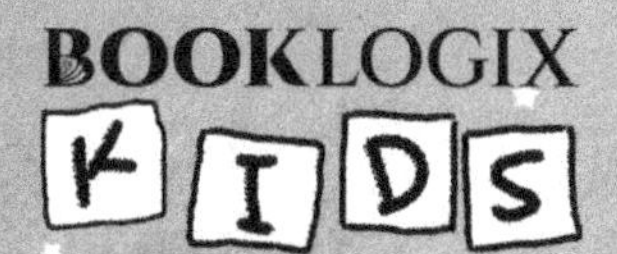

Alpharetta, Georgia

ISBN: 978-1-6653-0598-3 - Paperback
ISBN: 978-1-6653-0599-0 - Hardcover

Library of Congress Control Number: 2023900894

∞This paper meets the requirements of ANSI/NISO Z39.48-1992 (Permanence of Paper)

Illustrated by Joan Coleman, Ink Wonderland

0 7 1 1 2 3

For my sweet Charlotte and Jack.
May all your dreams come true.

When a monster
closes his eyes at night,

He doesn’t want to
dream of fright.

He dreams of a land far away,
where all he does is sing and play.

Why do I always
have to be scary?

I'd rather be a
flying fairy,

And sprinkle
stardust
on your head,

TOYS
As you sleep soundly in your bed.

I realize my
appearance is
quite alarming,
...oh my

But if you give me a chance,
I can be quite charming.

My fangs look sharp
and ready to bite,

But actually they're helpful while flying my kite.

Worried my horns
might buck you?

Fear not, I use them
to tie my shoe.

My claws seem long
and ready to tear,

But they work like a charm to comb my hair.

My feet are large
and smelly for sure,

Perhaps they'd be less
scary with a pedicure?

Making a big
ferocious roar,

Has become
quite a bore.

I’d rather be delightful and sweet,

And help bake
cupcakes and
other treats.

I'd love to come out
before it's spooky
and dark,
Boo!

And swing
and slide at
the sunny park.

So, I've found that being a monster is rather lonely.

I'm tired of being a "one and only."

I want to have
friends just
like you,

To eat ice cream with
and go to the zoo.

So when you begin
to imagine a scary
monster under
your bed,

Remember,
it's all in your head.

A monster is really
just like *you.*

They love kisses and snuggles from their mommy too.

The End

Catherine Pilcher Gayle lives in Atlanta, Georgia with her husband, Woody, and their two children. She's had a passion for creative writing since her childhood growing up in Dalton, Georgia. Catherine went on to attend the University of Georgia where she received a Business Degree in Risk Management-Insurance. After college, Catherine spent a summer in London, England, followed by working in New York City. Her love of these two cities gave her inspiration to write her upcoming chapter book series for early independent readers. Catherine's first published work, When a Monster Dreams, was written to help alleviate her young son's fear of monsters at bedtime. Her idea quickly expanded into a "monster series" touching on topics such as mindfulness and manners.

Catherine teaches preschool in Atlanta and receives creative inspiration from her students daily. Catherine's children, Charlotte and Jack, are her greatest joy in life and their favorite pastimes together include dressing up in costume and creating plays and fairytales. To learn more visit www.catgaylebooks.com.

Joan Coleman, an avid artist since childhood and a prolific professional artist for over 10 years, specializes in creating beautiful fashion-forward artwork for a variety of wonderful clients all over the world. Her trendy designs lend themselves well to home décor, apparel, and related merchandise and products. She is also a talented and versatile children's book illustrator having had the opportunity to work with several accomplished authors and publishers. Joan creates her artwork from her Oregon coast studio in the Pacific Northwest. She utilizes a wide variety of art techniques and mediums including acrylic paints, oil pastels, graphites, colored pencils, watercolors, inks, and digital design techniques to create her artwork and designs. She is known for her versatility and tenacious design strategy while simultaneously bridging the artistic gap between tradition and technology.

Milton Keynes UK
Ingram Content Group UK Ltd.
UKHW051851131023
430515UK00008B/46